THE WIND IN THE WILLOWS

I had flu. I was in the middle of Syria. It was three o'clock in the morning. The telephone rang and a producer who had miscalculated the time difference between London and Aleppo, asked me if I was interested in directing a movie of Kenneth Grahame's much-loved children's classic.

Some time later when I was back in London, I found to my surprise that the idea had taken root. There were two problems. The first was that I had never read *The Wind in the Willows*. The second was that I preferred Alan Bennett's excellent stage adaptation to the one that I was being offered. A third problem was that Alan's adaptation was already in production at Paramount. In fact, it turned out that there were no less than five or even six film versions of *The Wind in the Willows* currently in the pipeline. Unwittingly I had entered a race.

The reason for this burst of cinematic enthusiasm was not a wind of inspiration sweeping through like-minded film producers, but the fact that the author had been dead long enough for the story to have come out of copyright. The EC, however, was about to change European copyright laws and the book was about to go back into copyright again. So there was a sort of double race going on.

By the time the company that had first approached me decided not to go ahead (as so often happens) I had read the book and started to get a few ideas of my own about how to adapt it as a film, so I was sorry to see the project die. However a week later, the telephone rang while I was on the loo, and Jake Eberts said he'd heard I was interested in doing *The Wind in the Willows* and could we meet.

It was Jake who got the project going and whose faith in the thing saw it through to completion. I cannot thank him enough for the risk he took and for the enthusiasm with which he imbued the whole enterprise.

I would like to ask forgiveness of all those who think I've taken too many liberties with their favourite children's book. I would plead in mitigation that I've simply tried to turn *The Wind in the Willows* into a film in the same sort of way that A. A. Milne turned it into a stage play as *Toad of Toad Hall*. I only hope I have succeeded a tenth as well.

Terry Jones

London, January 1996

THE WIND IN THE WILLOWS

The complete illustrated screenplay
based on the book by Kenneth Grahame

TERRY JONES

Photographs by Keith Hamshere

Mandarin

We are flying high above the broad breast of England. Beneath us,
emerald green meadows, woods and copses, growing larger as we sweep
down towards one particular field . . . down and down until we reach tree
height and then down again . . . right down until we are level with the
grass and even then we carry on downwards . . . beneath the earth itself
until we come to rest on a distemper brush.

    We are in Mole's hole. A cosy hole. Mole is up a ladder, whitewashing
the ceiling. He hums contentedly to himself. The kettle whistles and the
clock says, 'Tea-time.'

MOLE. Oh good.

Suddenly the earth trembles. A thunder vibrates the air. The stepladder
wobbles. The paint pot spills, as a jagged scar appears across the virgin
white of the newly painted ceiling.

MOLE. What under earth . . . ?

Another violent shudder shakes his hole. A wall splits apart. Mole falls
off his ladder, picks himself up, grabs his miner's helmet and hurries out
into his 'garden' – full of statuary and works of art. Suddenly the roof
cracks: a corner subsides, statues fall over. His whole world is crumbling
about his ears. Mole runs up a tunnel.

Mole's head appears above ground. His eyesight is bad at the best of times and now he's dazzled by the sunlight. The noise is deafening. The world shakes. He can just make out vague monsters – fearful shapes in the blinding sun. Terrified, Mole runs across the meadow as an earthmover driven by a weasel crashes through the woodland.

Mole approaches the river. A bright point catches his eye and he sees a window and a front door built into the riverbank under a tree root. Suddenly Rat pops up.

RAT. Hullo, Mole.

MOLE *(peering myopically)*. Hullo, Rat?

RAT. Care for a mess about on the river?

MOLE. Oh dear, no no no . . . certainly not.

RAT. Good!

MOLE. No no, I can't . . . It's very kind of you, of course.

RAT. It's just the day for a picnic.

MOLE. I hate to bother you but . . . something terrible is going on.

RAT. Something 'terrible' going on?

He looks round at the beauty of the river. An otter breaks the surface, a fish in his mouth.

OTTER. Hello, Ratty!

RAT. Hello, Otter.

On the further bank a cycle tour of rabbits waves.

RABBITS. Yoo hoo!

RAT. Careful, you rabbits!

The sun itself turns a kindly face towards Rat.

SUN. Beautiful day!

RAT. Beautiful day! *(He turns back to Mole.)* My dear Mole,

there's not the minutest thing terrible going on. It's a lovely, glorious day for a picnic. Jump in.

MOLE. It is a lovely day, except my home has been knocked in.

RAT. Who 'knocked in' your hole, Mole?

MOLE. That's what I'm going to ask Mr Toad.

RAT. Toad?

MOLE. It was in his meadow . . .

RAT. You won't get any sense out of Toad. Whereas a picnic might steady the nerves.

MOLE. It wasn't very grand, but it was my home.

RAT. You can move in with me, Mole.

MOLE. And I did love it so, Rat.

RAT. But the hamper's all packed and . . . *(He is moved by Mole's plight.)* Oh come on . . . I'll take you to Toad Hall.

MOLE. Thank you, Rat.

RAT. We can have the picnic there. *(The boat rocks as he helps Mole in.)* Mind the paintwork!

The sensation of being in a boat takes Mole over.

MOLE. I've never been in a boat before.

RAT *(his whiskers crinkling)*. What? Never been in a . . . you never . . . well, shiver me whiskers! *(He straightens them.)* You poor creature!

MOLE. Is it as nice as all that?

RAT. Nice? It's the only thing! Believe me, my young friend, there is *nothing* – absolutely nothing – half as worth doing as simply messing about in boats. Simply messing . . . messing . . . about . . . in . . . boats . . .

RAT *(in a day-dream, singing).*

There's plenty to do and lots of time too,
Messing about on the river.
Wherever you go, you go with the flow
When you're messing about on the river.
Whether you get there or whether you don't
You think it would matter – I tell you it won't.
There's lots to be done and it's all of it fun
Messing about on the river.

THE RIVER.

I'm on my way to the sea.
Come with me!
I'm on my way to the sea.

Rat and Mole row down the river, drinking in the natural beauty that surrounds them.

MOLE. But surely you can't spend your whole life *just* messing about on the river?

RAT. By it and with it and on it and in it. It's brother and sister to me, and company, and food and drink. The river's my world, and I don't want any other. What it hasn't got is not worth having and what it doesn't know is not worth knowing.

MOLE. What's *that*?

Mole points to the Wild Wood. It is dark and forbidding. Rat's manner darkens too.

RAT. That? That's the Wild Wood. We don't go there very much – we river-bankers.

MOLE. Why? Aren't they . . . aren't they very nice p-p-people in there?

RAT. W-e-ll . . . The squirrels are all right. And the rabbits – some of 'em. And there's Badger, of course. He lives right in the heart of it. Dear old Badger. But it's not for the likes of you or me.

MOLE. Why-why-why not?

Weasels peer out of the Wild Wood.

RAT. Well, there are others . . . er . . . weasels especially. They're all right in their way – but they're just out for themselves – don't give a hoot for anyone else . . .

MOLE. And beyond the Wild Wood?

Rat follows his gaze towards the horizon: the odd puff of smoke, a town far away and a distant steam train.

> RAT. Beyond the Wild Wood comes the Wide World. And that's something that doesn't matter either to you or to me. Don't ever refer to it again, please.

In the Wild Wood, two weasels peer out of the undergrowth. They are stuffing something into an already wriggling sack.

> CLARENCE WEASEL. Rat thinks life's one big picnic.
> GEOFFREY WEASEL. Wait till *we* take over the river bank. He won't find it so easy then!
> CLARENCE WEASEL *(to the sack)*. Keep still in there! *(Voice in the sack: 'Y-y-yes, s-s-s-sir. S-s-s-sorry, s-s-s-sir.')*

Back on the river, Rat stops rowing for a moment and nods towards Toad Hall.

> RAT. There's Toad Hall now. Finest house on the river, though we never admit as much to Toad.

They glide up to the jetty. Mole is captivated. Rat notices a pile of abandoned and sunk boats.

> RAT. Hello! The boating craze is over. First it was sailing. Then he tired of that and took to punting. This year I've been giving him skulling lessons.

Across the wide sweep of lawn in front of Toad Hall, a white shape can be seen flapping in the breeze. It is a map, which is being studied by someone. A mayfly passes by. The map is lowered to reveal Toad who watches the mayfly for a moment and then flicks out a long, long, prehensile tongue, catches the mayfly and swallows it. Suddenly he sees Rat and Mole.

> TOAD. Hooray! Splendid!
> RAT. Toad, this is Mole.
> TOAD *(pumping Mole's hand)*. Just going to send for you – both of you.
> RAT. My young friend has just lost his home.
> TOAD. Has he? What a stroke of luck!
> MOLE. Oh no! It was dreadful.
> TOAD. You can come and live with me.
> RAT. He's coming to live with *me*, Toad.
> TOAD. But I've just acquired the very thing. Come and see!

Toad sets off into the house, the others catch up.

RAT. How's the boating?

TOAD. Boating! Pooh! Silly boyish amusement. Given that up
   long ago.

*Toad disappears into the house. Rat and Mole have to follow. Inside
Toad Hall, the family portraits look disapprovingly down from the walls.*

TOAD. Finest house on the river – what?

Rat exchanges glances with Mole.

MOLE. I was hoping you'd help me get my home back.

RAT. It was in your meadow, you see, Toad.

TOAD. Not my meadow any longer . . .

*They are standing each side of a particularly disapproving ancestor's bust.
The eyes flick open. Toad puts his hands over the bust's ears.*

TOAD *(whispering)*. Sold it off. Needed a spot of ready cash.

MOLE *(looking aghast at Rat)*. He 'sold off' my hole?

RAT. Now look here, Toad . . .

But Toad has gone. They chase after him.

RAT. That meadow belonged to your father. Moles have lived in it for centuries – you've no business just selling it off like . . .

Toad leads the way into his stableyard.

TOAD. Behold! Your new home, Moley.

A canary-coloured gypsy caravan stands in the yard, with a horse between the shafts.

MOLE *(peering myopically)*. What is it?
HORSE. Very heavy.
TOAD. It's the lastest thing!
MOLE *(aside to Rat)*. I don't want a *new* home, Ratty.

Toad leaps around and becomes the proud proprietor/salesman. He pops up all over the caravan.

TOAD. The open road, the dusty highway, heath and hedgerow and rolling downs! Here today, up and off to somewhere else tomorrow!
HORSE *(groans and slumps in its shafts)*. It doesn't bear thinking about.

MOLE. It's a caravan.
TOAD. Finest cart ever built! Designed it myself, of course. *(A table shoots out from the back of the caravan – all fully set for luncheon.)* And we can set off after lunch.
RAT. Now just stop right there, Toady.
TOAD. Travel, change, excitement!
RAT. Did I hear you say 'we' and 'start' and 'after lunch'?
TOAD. Dear Ratty, you can't just stick to your fusty old river all your life. I want to show you the world!
RAT. I don't want to see the world. And I *am* going to stick to my fusty old river – Mole and I are going for a picnic on it. Aren't we, Mole?

MOLE. Well, yes . . . when I've found out what happened to my home . . .
RAT. Absolutely.
TOAD. Then it's settled. We set off after lunch!

Rat and Mole exchange looks.

HORSE. It's not just the weight . . . it's the constant jumping up and down and going, 'I say, horsey! Faster!'

It is a golden afternoon. The sun hums to himself and there are sounds of mass kissing in the air. The cycle tour of rabbits, snogging by the roadside, pause to watch the caravan pass.

TOAD. I say, horsey! Faster!

Toad tugs on the reins and jumps up and down.

HORSE. See what I mean?

Mole and Rat are trotting alongside talking confidentially.

MOLE. It's very kind of Mr Toad, of course, but it's not like having my own home.
RAT. Don't worry, he'll soon get bored with it.

The caravan turns on to the smooth high road. Toad is bored.

RAT. Toad, when you say you sold off your meadow . . . Who did you sell it to?
TOAD *(airily)*. Oh, some weasels I believe.
RAT. *Weasels*! Toad!
TOAD. Now don't start lecturing me.
RAT. You know the weasels are after Toad Hall.
TOAD. It was only a meadow.
RAT. It was Mole's home.
TOAD. Pooh! You worry too much, Ratty.

Mole, who is walking behind, stiffens. There is a distant roar, a horn blaring . . . louder . . . and louder . . . Suddenly a motor car is on them.

MOLE *(diving for the ditch)*. Look out!

The motor swerves violently. A flash of glittering plate glass, rich morocco leatherwork and walnut veneer. The horn blares. The horse rears. The motor disappears as the caravan topples into the ditch.

RAT. Villains! Scoundrels! Road-hogs!

Mole runs to help Rat right the cart. The horse kicks and rears.

RAT. Toad! Come and give us a hand. Toad?

They turn and see a dust-covered Toad sitting in the road. His collar is awry but his face wears a seraphic smile.

TOAD. Poop-poop! Poop-poop!
RAT. Are you all right, Toady?
TOAD. Poop-poop!
RAT. There. It's gone now.
TOAD. Glorious, stirring sight!

Rat and Mole pick Toad up and dust him down.

RAT. We'll go straight to the police station and lodge a complaint . . .
TOAD. Police station? Complaint? Me *complain* of that beautiful . . . heavenly vision?
RAT. The cart's not too badly damaged . . .
TOAD. *Carts?* Pooh! Horrid little carts – common carts – canary-coloured carts!

Toad has sat down again in the road in a happy dream.

TOAD. The poetry of motion! The *real* way to travel! Here today – in next week tomorrow! WHEEEEEEE!

Suddenly a wind hits his face. Toad pulls down a pair of goggles and we realise he is now speeding along in a spanking new car. He drives like a maniac along country lanes, flinging the car left and right. Mole and Rat are in the back – petrified.

TOAD. Villages skipped, towns and cities jumped – OOPS! Always somebody else's horizon! Oh, bliss! Oh, poop-poop!

RAT. Toad! For goodness' sake, slow down!

TOAD. POOP-POOP! POOP-POOP!

Toad leans over to poop the horn on the far side of the car.

RAT. Toad!

Toad swerves to miss a hay-cart, smashes through a gate, ploughs across a field, through a hedge, across another road, through two fences, over another field and on into the Wild Wood.

RAT. Stop, Toad!

Geoffrey and Clarence Weasel are frisking some terrified rabbits. St John Weasel is riffling through a field mouse's wallet. They look up as the car smashes through the undergrowth.

    RAT. Stop!

A low branch catches Rat and yanks him out of the car. Mole leaps up to see what's happened.

    MOLE. Ratty!

The car hits a log, and Mole is flung out too. Toad has no concept of braking and the motor car plunges on.

    TOAD. Hang on . . . *(Noticing his lack of passengers.)* I say, I wonder where *they* went? . . . Ooooh!

The car disappears over a ridge. A moment later there is a crash. The motor car has jack-knifed against a tree. Toad's legs stick up from the back seat.

In another part of the Wild Wood, the sinister figure of the Chief Weasel sits at a tree stump, counting out protection money from a line of rabbits. Clarence and Godfrey Weasel arrive, breathless.

CLARENCE WEASEL. Chief! Toad's crashed another motor car!

GEOFFREY WEASEL. That's his seventh he's smashed!

CHIEF WEASEL. That green-head's playing right into our hands.

It is dusk in the Wild Wood. Mole is bent over the ground, looking for his glasses.

SUN. Cheerio!

The friendly face of the sun is disappearing behind a hill.

MOLE. Oh. Wait a minute!
SUN. Sorry. Can't stop!

The sun sets, humming to itself. Night falls over the Wild Wood. Suddenly the Chief Weasel and his gang appear.

CHIEF WEASEL. Well, well, if it isn't a little mole.
MOLE. I'm n-n-not afraid of you weasels! My friends will be here any minute.
ST JOHN WEASEL. 'Friends'?
MOLE *(small voice).* Yes.
CHIEF WEASEL. Listen, Mole. There are no such things in this world as 'friends'.
ST JOHN WEASEL. Everyone's only out for themselves.
CHIEF WEASEL. Take us weasels ...

The Chief Weasel ushers Mole on his way. The weasels fall alongside in a sort of dance routine.

WEASELS.
> First you see us . . .
> Then you don't . . .
> > *(They disappear.)*
> Now you hear us . . .
> > *(The next whispered.)*
> Now you won't.
> > *(They suddenly reappear making Mole jump.)*
> It's our secret of survival
> In a Very Nasty World.

Mole is suddenly covered by disembodied hands.

> Now you feel us . . .
> Now you can't.
> Are we real?

The weasels suddenly disintegrate like cartoon cut-outs.

> Perhaps we aren't!
> It's our secret of survival
> In a Very Nasty World!
> It's our secret of survival
> In a Very Nasty World.

MOLE. Is it really *such* a nasty world?

CHIEF WEASEL. Oh yes! A very nasty world *indeed*!

OTHER WEASELS. Nastier than you could *ever* dream of!

The weasels appear out of a tree in front of Mole's face, and out of the ground – just where he was about to tread, etc.

WEASELS.
> From up above . . .
> And from beneath . . .
> Eyes and jaws . . .
> Claws and teeth.
>
> Ready to attack you.
> You're a snack – you'd better run!

CHIEF WEASEL *(his face close up to Mole's)*
> Don't come walking in the Wild Wood
> If you haven't got a gun!

The weasels all laugh maniacally. Mole collapses in a gibbering heap.
They dance around poking him, and (when they are not looking) each
other. It starts to snow.

WEASELS.

> Every creature for survival
> Has to look out for itself!
> Got no nannies here or grannies, dear,
> To look after your health.
>
> You're in the Wild Wood!
> And every child could
> Tell you that you got no
> Business to here!
> Wooooooooooooooooh!

As the weasels dance about singing, the snow falls thicker. Suddenly Rat's voice is heard.

RAT. Mole! Are you there, Mole? MOLE!

The weasels all look at each other uneasily.

CHIEF WEASEL. Listen, Mole. You tell your 'friends' to stop meddling in Toad's affairs.

ST JOHN WEASEL. Yes. It's our meadow and we're going to build a really big . . .

CHIEF WEASEL. Shut up! *(To Mole.)* If Toad wants to sell his property to us that's *his* business . . .

ST JOHN WEASEL. Right! And when he sells us Toad Hall *we'll* call the shots round here . . .

CHIEF WEASEL. Why don't you tell him *all* our plans?

ST JOHN WEASEL *(the sarcasm is lost on him)*. Well, first we make Toad Hall a weasel-only area. Then we'll ban picnics along the whole river bank . . .

CHIEF WEASEL. Garbage brain!

The Chief Weasel hits St John Weasel so hard he flies across the glade. The other weasels snigger.

CHIEF WEASEL. It's meant to be a *secret*!

RAT. Mole! It's old Rat!

CHIEF WEASEL. 'Friends'! You're a spineless nobody, Mole! Who'd want to be *your* 'friend'?

The weasels disappear.

RAT. Mole! Where are you, Moley?

Mole tries to call but can't. Snow falls across his face, then a tear. Suddenly a rather battered Rat is shaking him.

RAT. You all right, Mole?

MOLE. I am now you're here, Ratty.

RAT *(lifting Mole to his feet and brushing the snow off him)*. Tuck your scarf in. Don't want to catch cold. We'd better find Toad. It's not safe in the Wild Wood, not safe at all . . .

Night has fallen. Toad, all alone, is wandering about the Wild Wood in a trance. Eyes watch him. Some sniggering.

TOAD. Poop-poop! Poop-poop!

VOICE. PARP-PARP!

TOAD *(comes out of his trance)*. Poo-er . . . W-W-Who's there?

There is maniacal laughter. Toad goes weak at the knees. Suddenly the Chief Weasel appears over his shoulder.

CHIEF WEASEL. Mr Toad.

TOAD. Argh! It's you!

CHIEF WEASEL. What an honour for the Wild Wood.

TOAD. Good lord! How did I get *here*?

CHIEF WEASEL. I understand you need finance for another motor car?

TOAD. Another motor . . . yes . . .

CHIEF WEASEL. We have a little business proposition . . .

Rat and Mole are lost in the dark, snow-bound wood.

MOLE. Oh, Ratty. We aren't lost, are we?

RAT. No, no . . . This way, old fellow . . .

They plough on, clearly lost. Suddenly they come across Badger's house.

RAT *(pointing)*. Brace up, Moley! It's Badger's place.

Mole nervously eyes the sign: MR BADGER. STRICTLY NO VISITORS. *Rat rings the bell.*

RAT. Don't worry – Badger's not that fierce.

MOLE. 'Fierce'?

It is dark inside Badger's house. We hear snores. By a fire sits a figure with a newspaper over his face.

BADGER. What the devil . . .!

From deep down in the earth there are sounds of grunting and shuffling around, doors being unlocked. Gradually a grumbling voice approaches. Badger appears, illuminating the burrow with a lantern. We see both the interior and the exterior simultaneously: the warm and glowing light within and the cold, snow-driven night without.

Outside, Rat and Mole listen intently. Inside, Badger peers suspiciously at the door. He is not in a good mood. He moves an inch nearer and listens. Rat and Mole move an inch nearer and listen. Badger moves closer. Rat and Mole move closer.

Badger puts his ear up against the door. Rat bangs the knocker loudly. Badger jumps out of his skin – his ear-drum throbs.

BADGER *(flings the door open)*. What is the meaning of this?!
MOLE. Oh, er.
BADGER. Can't you read the notice?
RAT. Sorry, Badger. It's me – Ratty . . .
BADGER. It's the middle of winter!
RAT . . . and my friend Mole.
BADGER. *And* the middle of the night by the looks of it!
RAT. We're lost in the Wild Wood.
BADGER. Hmph! It's you, you say, Rat?
RAT. Well . . . Obviously, Badger.
BADGER. And 'Mole'?

Mole quails as Badger peers hostilely at him.

MOLE *(very small voice indeed)*. Y-y-y-yes . . . ssssir.
BADGER. Then you'd better come in.
RAT. Thank you, Badger.

Badger hustles them in and ushers them down the tunnel to the kitchen. It is very cosy. The floor is of ruddy brick, the ceiling is hung with hams, bundles of dried herbs, nets of onions and baskets of eggs. A fire roars on a wide hearth flanked by two oaken settles, shiny with long wear.

BADGER. Were the weasels beastly to you, Moley?
MOLE. They said they were going to turn Toad Hall into a weasel-only area.
BADGER. Did they.

MOLE. And ban picnics on the river . . .

RAT. Ban *picnics*?

MOLE. And they're building a big 'something' on the
meadow Toad sold them.

BADGER. Toad sold his meadow to the *weasels*?

MOLE. That's why they kn-knocked in my house . . .
(He starts to sob.)

BADGER *(comforting him)*. It's all right, Moley – you can come
and live with me . . .

RAT. He's going to live with me, Badger.

MOLE. It was only a shabby, dingy little place – not like here,
Badger, or your cosy quarters, Rat, or Toad's beautiful Hall,
but it was my own . . . my very own . . . little . . . hole . . .

BADGER. That good-for-nothing Toad!

RAT. Now he's crashed yet another motor car.

BADGER. How many's that?

RAT. Crashes or cars? Oh well, it's the same thing
with Toad. This is the seventh.

There is a frenzied ringing on the doorbell.

BADGER. What the – ? This is an outrage!

A terrified Toad is pulling the front doorbell. The door opens.

BADGER. Now, I've had quite enough visitors for one winter.

Toad collapses into Badger's arms.
Some time later, Rat and Mole have propped the gibbering Toad in front of the fire.

BADGER. Oh, pull yourself together, Toad.

TOAD. I was attacked by w-w-w-w-weasels – half a dozen of them!

MOLE. Did they sing a dreadful song?

TOAD. They wanted me to put up Toad Hall as collateral against a new motor.

RAT. Toad! You didn't . . .

TOAD. Of course not! The old place is worth six cars at least.

BADGER. 'Six motor cars'! It's time you stopped this motoring craze.

RAT. It costs the earth, Toady.

BADGER. You've squandered the money your father left you . . .

TOAD. Haven't. There's tons of it!

BADGER. Your father was a particular friend of mine, Toad. I promised him on his deathbed I would ensure you looked after your inheritance.

TOAD. I'm only having a bit of fun.

BADGER. Sir, you are a nincompoop!

TOAD. Kind of you to say so, Badger.

RAT. Nincompoop is *not* a compliment, Toad.

TOAD. Isn't it?

BADGER. Take off those ridiculous goggles.

TOAD. Shan't.

BADGER. Rat?

Rat hesitates, then takes the goggles off Toad and gives them to Badger who tosses them on the fire.

TOAD. Oh, I say, Badger!

BADGER. And now the driving gloves.

TOAD. Oh, not my driving gloves!

BADGER. Take them off.

TOAD. But they're brand new. Cost a fortune! *(He realises he's let the cat out of the bag.)*

BADGER. Exactly.

As his driving gloves burn, Toad's spirit evaporates too.

BADGER. Now, young man, you will accompany me into the smoking room, to hear one or two facts about yourself.

Badger escorts the humbled Toad into the smoking room. Rat and Mole poke the fire and gaze into the flames. The firelight dances on the plates and pots and pans and on the grandfather clock, ticking in the corner. As time passes, they hear weeping and moaning coming from the smoking room, and then Badger and Toad's voices.

TOAD. You're right, Badger. I have been both foolish and feckless.

BADGER. Toad Hall is your sacred trust, Toad.

TOAD. Yes. Yes.

BADGER. If the weasels were ever to get their hands on it . . . then . . . it would be the end of the river bank as we know it . . .

An hour later, Mole and Rat wake as Badger and a very small and chastened Toad emerge. His legs are wobbly, and he's been crying buckets.

BADGER *(kindly)*. My friends, I am pleased to inform you that Toad has something important to say to you both. Sit down, Toad. *(Toad meekly sits.)* Right, Toad.

He nods to Toad to speak, but Toad remains silent.

BADGER. Start with the 'How sorry I am' bit.

Toad looks desperately for some means of escape.

BADGER. 'Oh, how sorry I am that I have been foolish and . . .'

TOAD. But I'm *not* sorry. And it wasn't foolish at all. It was simply glorious!

BADGER. But – didn't you just tell me in there . . .

TOAD. Oh, yes yes – in *there* – I'd have said anything in *there*.

BADGER. You back-sliding animal.

TOAD. Dear Badger – you're so eloquent – you can do what you like with me in *there*. But I've been thinking it over out *here* and I find that out here I'm not the least bit sorry, so it's no earthly good saying I am, now is it?

BADGER. Then you *don't* promise never to touch a motor car ever again?

TOAD. On the contrary, I faithfully promise that the very first motor car I see – poop-poop! Off I go in it!

Badger rises majestically to his feet.

BADGER. Gentlemen. It's Plan B.
RAT. Plan B? What's that, Badger?

Badger grabs Toad and bundles him into a hamper.

TOAD. I say! Unhand me!
BADGER. If you behave like a nincompoop, we'll have to *treat* you like a nincompoop.
TOAD. What are you doing?

Badger bangs the lid down, and locks the padlock. Silence. Then all hell breaks loose as Toad tries to burst out.

TOAD. Let me out! What is the meaning of this?
BADGER. Would you gentlemen give me a hand?

Rat and Mole are carrying the hamper containing Toad through another part of Badger's burrow.

TOAD. Put me down! This is abduction!
BADGER. Oh, do keep quiet, Toad!
RAT (*twitchy – he doesn't like it underground*). How much further, Badger?
BADGER. This tunnel will take us as far as Toad Hall itself. We're under his meadow now.

They are walking down a paved tunnel into which bits of masonry protrude: vaultings, pillars and arches.

MOLE. How under earth did you find time to do all this, Badger?
BADGER (*enjoying Mole's appreciation*). I didn't . . . Long, long ago there was a city of humans – right here. They thought their city would endure forever, but humans can't let things rest – they get greedy – that's their undoing. But we remain. There were badgers here before and there are badgers here still.
MOLE. Listen!

The terrible noises we heard earlier come from above. The tunnel shakes. A split appears in the roof and a wall collapses revealing a space, from which rolls a pot of whitewash. Mole stares at it. Grimly he takes Badger's lantern and steps through into the remains of his old home – now wrecked. Tears well up in his eyes. The others put their arms around him.

RAT. We'll teach those weasels . . . Moley.

Mole suddenly feels the strength of their comradeship.

Badger, Rat and Mole continue their underground journey, reach a jetty by an underground canal and climb into a boat. They emerge from the tunnels to find themselves on the moat of Toad Hall. They arrive at some steps and drag the hamper containing Toad up them.

TOAD *(from inside the hamper)*. Help, help! I'm being abducted!
BADGER. Keep quiet, Toad. You don't want your servants to hear you.
TOAD. Is this Toad Hall?
RAT. Ssh!
TOAD. I'll be the laughing stock of the kitchen.
BADGER. Then keep quiet.

A stranger, a salesman by the look of him, is talking to a hedgehog maid. He accosts them.

SALESMAN. I'm looking for a Mr Toad.
TOAD *(from inside the basket)*. He's not here.

The salesman looks puzzled. Badger and company go round a corner and stare in horror at what they see. The salesman joins them.

SALESMAN. I have *six* new motor cars for him.

There, indeed, are six spanking new, shiny motor cars.

RAT. Toad!
BADGER. You wretched animal.
TOAD. My new motors. Oh, I must see them! Let me out this instant!

The salesman looks in some surprise at the basket.

BADGER. Mr Toad will not be requiring *any* new motor cars.

TOAD. Yes, I do. I *love* them! Let me out!

RAT. He's not well.

TOAD. Oooh, I can see them! They're whoppers. Hooray!

BADGER. I'm afraid Mr Toad is not in a fit state to order anything.

TOAD. Yes, I am.

BADGER. He's suffering from a mania brought about by motor cars.

TOAD. It's not a mania. I *love* motor cars!

BADGER. As his physician I have ordered him to be locked away in his room until this mania has run its course.

Mole and Rat hurry the voluble hamper inside the house.

TOAD. Motor cars are my life! My soul! My *raison d'être*!

The servants stop and stare.

SALESMAN *(waving an order form)*. Mr Toad owes me money.

BADGER *(becoming confidential)*. Can I make a proposition?

SALESMAN. We're always open to a deal.

BADGER. How's this then? If you remove these hideous machines forthwith I promise *not* to insert *any* part of them into *any* portion of *your* anatomy.

The salesman thinks this over as if considering a deal. Badger means what he says.

SALESMAN. Right . . . Fair enough. Nice to do business with you, sir.

He climbs in a car and drives off with the others in tow. Badger tears up the order form. Meanwhile, in Toad's bedroom, Mole and Rat have opened the hamper. Toad leaps out and rushes to the window. He gives a howl of disappointment.

TOAD. They're driving off. My lovely motors. Stop them somebody! *(He collapses in a sobbing heap.)*

The weasels peer from the snow-covered bushes in Toad's garden.

CHIEF WEASEL. So Badger thinks he can cure Toad of motor cars, does he?

ST JOHN WEASEL. We don't want him to do that, Chief.

CHIEF WEASEL. I know . . .

ST JOHN WEASEL. We want Toad to spend every last penny he's got . . .

CHIEF WEASEL. I *know*!

ST JOHN WEASEL. So he has to give us Toad Hall . . .

CHIEF WEASEL. Why are you telling *me*?

ST JOHN WEASEL. I . . . er . . .

CHIEF WEASEL. Cheese-brain!

CLARENCE WEASEL. Chief! I'll make sure Toad doesn't forget about motor cars.

GEOFFREY WEASEL. Yes. We have a plan.

CLARENCE WEASEL. *I* have a plan.

GEOFFREY WEASEL. We both thought of it!

CLARENCE WEASEL. No, you didn't!

CHIEF WEASEL. Just do it!

Two weasels stick a 'Diversion' sign in the middle of the road pointing into the main gates of Toad Hall. A car is approaching. The weasels hide and watch it duly swing round into Toad Hall.

In his bedroom, Toad is sitting on a stool looking terrible – he's going through cold turkey. Rat is keeping watch over him. Suddenly Toad hears the car outside. He rushes to the window and his face becomes animated as he watches the car pass the door and out of the other gates.

Some time later, Toad has constructed a makeshift car out of a few chairs and is driving furiously as ever. Rat watches anxiously.

TOAD. Poop-poop! Poop-poop! Look out! Poop-poop! Officer! Get out of the way! Nincompoop! No! Arggh!

Toad swerves, falls off his chair, and lies there panting.

RAT. Seems to be a lot of traffic today, Toad. That's the third crash this morning. *(He helps Toad to his bed.)* I wish you'd get better, Toady. It's been months now.

TOAD. Perhaps if I . . . But no, I mustn't ask . . .

RAT. What?

TOAD. I was just thinking I might improve with a little fresh air . . .

RAT. No. I can't let you set foot outside this room.

TOAD. Quite right, Rat. Although I was only thinking of a little stroll along . . . the river.

Toad has hit a nerve. Rat goes dreamy. He sees the river.

RAT. The *river*! It's beautiful in the snow.

TOAD. But you're right. I should stay here safe indoors . . . Besides – you can't have a picnic in the middle of winter.

Bingo! He's got Rat in the bag. Rat's whiskers crinkle.

RAT. But you can! Everyone thinks you can't but you can have a picnic any time! In fact, winter picnics are my speciality. A hot thermos. A warm rug. I know the perfect hollow where we could get snug and look out at the snow . . .

TOAD. If anything could take my mind off – you know what . . .

RAT. Quite, quite! A picnic on the river would *certainly* do it. A winter picnic, too.

TOAD. And there's a picnic hamper in the cellar . . . all ready . . .

RAT. No, no, Toad. I can't . . .

TOAD. It might be the very cure.

RAT. Well, it would. A picnic on the river cures anything. Toad . . . If you promise me faithfully to behave . . .

TOAD. Oh, you know me, Ratty.

RAT. A picnic on the river! Why didn't we think of it before?

TOAD. You'll have to go right down to the cellar to get the hamper.

Rat starts to leave. He hesitates at the door.

RAT. Look, Toad, best not mention anything about this to
  Badger.

TOAD. Wouldn't dream of it, old chap.

*Rat leaves. He locks the door carefully behind him. For a moment he has
second thoughts, but then he hears the wind in the willows and the
moorhen calling. His mind is filled with images of the river. He turns and
runs downstairs.*

Alone in his bedroom, Toad grins and begins to sing.

TOAD.
>   Oh, the clever men at Oxford
>   Know all that there is to be knowed,
>   But they none of them know one half as much
>   As clever old Mr Toad!

*Toad flings a bed sheet out of the window, and clambers down. At the
bottom he does a little dance and sings again.*

>   The world has held great heroes,
>   As history books have showed,
>   But never a name to go down to fame
>   Compared with that of Toad!

As he prances off down the road, the weasels watch.

>   The army all saluted
>   As they marched along the road . . .

Toad gazes up at the swinging sign of a country inn. He suddenly realises he's rather hungry. With a sigh of self-satisfaction, he turns into the inn humming to himself. Clarence and Geoffrey Weasel emerge from behind a tree and set a sign reading 'Road Closed Ahead' outside the inn.

Inside the inn, Toad is just finishing an extravagant meal when a certain sound makes his eyes pop.

TOAD *(under his breath)*. Poop-poop!

Toad conceals himself under the window ledge and peers out. A motor car approaches. It stops at the 'Road Closed' sign.

JUSTIN. Bother!

SAMANTHA. What rotten luck!

GERVAIS *(noticing the inn)*. Ah, well! Might as well have a spot of lunch.

The motoring party stroll into the inn.

JUSTIN. Landlord! A table in the snug, if you'd be so kind.

They are ushered through and Toad emerges from hiding. He reaches over the partition for their driving goggles. He is drawn to the door. There stands the motor car, expensive, glittering – and unattended! Toad confronts his dream. He touches it. His breath comes shorter . . . in a trance, his hands run over the mudguards.

TOAD. Oh my, oh my, oh my.

He feels down the radiator and finds the centre of pleasure – the starting handle. An electric thrill shoots through him.

TOAD. I wonder if they'd *sell* it? Of course, I'd need to test it first . . . Just to be quite certain I *really* liked it . . .

Toad cranks it. The engine springs into life. Toad is ecstatic. He leaps into the driving seat.

TOAD. Ahhhh! Just a little spin . . .

He sets off, knocking over the 'Road Closed' sign.

Oh my . . . oh my . . . oh my . . .

It's Toad on the road! The weasels watch with bated breath.

TOAD. Look out! It's Toad! The Terror of the Trail!
    The Fastest Toad on the Road! Stand back! Poop-poop!
    POOP-POOP!

He careers wildly round the corner. There is a loud crash. The motoring party appear – serviettes under their chins, knives and forks in their hands. They gape in silent dismay.

The scene shifts abruptly to a courtroom.

FIRST BARRISTER. The full penalty of the law can hardly be sufficient for the heinous, callous, unmitigatedly evil crime perpetrated by the despicable rogue whom we now see cowering before us in the dock.

He points an accusing finger at the cowering Toad. Weasels in the gallery applaud and cheer.

FIRST BARRISTER. I rest my case.

JUDGE. I thought you were meant to be Counsel for the Defence?

FIRST BARRISTER. Yes, Your Honour. I *am* defending, but this crime is so blaggardly, that this is the best defence that can be offered.

JUDGE. I see. Er, Counsel for the Prosecution, do you wish to add anything to what the Counsel for the Defence has said?

SECOND BARRISTER. No, milud. I would just like to *wag* my finger at the accused a few times.

JUDGE. Of course.

The second barrister rises and proceeds to wag his finger at Toad, who cowers dutifully.

SECOND BARRISTER. Thank you, milud.

JUDGE. You're welcome. Are there any witnesses for the Defence?

FIRST BARRISTER *(jumping up, outraged)*. How can there be, milud? It's an open and shut case! He even insulted an officer of the law.

Gasps from the gallery.

POLICEMAN. He called me a 'nincompoop'.

FIRST BARRISTER. I demand the severest sentence you can think of!

Clarence and Geoffrey Weasel shout, 'Hear, hear!' from the gallery.

JUDGE. It's not *much* of a defence, is it?

FIRST BARRISTER. The best that can be done in the circumstances, milud. *(He swings round and points an accusing finger at Toad.)* See! The very word GUILTY stamped across his brow!

The weasels whistle and stamp their feet in appreciation.

TOAD. Oh er . . . Couldn't the Prosecution say something else?

JUDGE. Silence!

Amongst the spectators are the motoring party, and Rat, Mole and Badger, who look uncomfortable at being in the Wide World.

BADGER. Hmph. May I speak on behalf of the defendant?

WEASELS. No! Boo! Sit down!

JUDGE. Do you really want to? Oh, very well.

BADGER. Thank you, milud. The gentleman you see before you, Toad, has not been in his right mind for some·time.

TOAD *(sulkily)*. Have.

RAT. Shut up, Toady!

JUDGE. Silence in court!

BADGER. He is suffering from a *dementia* – a form of madness . . .

TOAD. It's not madness!

BADGER . . . brought about by motor cars . . .

TOAD. Motors are what make life worth living! The speed! The thrill! I'll never stop it! It's simply glorious! *(He is rapped on the head by the policeman's truncheon.)*

BADGER. That's it! That's the last time I ever try to help that worthless . . . *(He leaves.)*

JUDGE *(banging his gavel)*. I've heard enough! Before I pronounce sentence would the jury care to find the prisoner guilty?

The jury are all frightened-looking rabbits – except for one.

RAT. I object! One of those rabbits is a weasel.

CHIEF WEASEL. No, I'm not! I'm a rabbit.

RAT. He's never a rabbit!

JUDGE *(to other rabbits)*. Is he a rabbit?

CHIEF WEASEL *(under his breath)*. Say I'm a rabbit . . .

JURY *(scared to death)*. Yes-yes-yes! He's a rabbit all right!

JUDGE. And how do you find the accused?

WEASELS. GUILTY!

JUDGE. I'm asking the jury!

CHIEF WEASEL *(under his breath)*. Say guilty.

JURY. G-g-guilty.

JUDGE. Good! Then I condemn Toad to be taken from this place to a place of lawful execution and hanged by the . . .

The clerk of the court whispers in the judge's ear.

JUDGE *(disappointed)*. Can't I? Oh well, I sentence Toad to as long in jail as I possibly can . . .

CLERK OF THE COURT. Say twelve months for theft, three years for dangerous driving and fifteen years for cheeking a police officer.

POLICEMAN. He called me a 'nincompoop'.

CLERK OF THE COURT. So you've told us before.

POLICEMAN. 'Nincompoop' – me!

JUDGE. That's eighteen, nineteen – let's make it a round twenty years in the rankest jail in the kingdom! Has the prisoner anything to say?

TOAD. Yes. Nincompoop!

JUDGE. What!

TOAD. You're all nincompoops!

RAT. Toad!

POLICEMAN. What did I tell you? *(He hits Toad again.)*

JUDGE. I increase it to twenty-five years!

TOAD. What do you know about life – about freedom? You're all miserable, one-eyed *nincompoops*!

JUDGE. Thirty years!

TOAD. What right have you to judge *me*?

JUDGE. Take him away! No! Wait!

TOAD. I am Toad! The Great Toad!

JUDGE. FORTY YEARS!

TOAD. The Handsome Toad! The Unstoppable Toad!

Toad leaps up on to the side of the prisoner's box. He sings.

TOAD.

> The world has held great heroes,
> As history books have showed;
> But never a name to go down to fame
> Compared with that of Toad.

JUDGE. FIFTY YEARS!

*Toad skips from the prisoner's box to the witness box to the jury box –
brilliantly evading the arms of the court officials.*

TOAD.

> The army all saluted
> As they marched along the road,
> Was it the king? Or president?
> No. It was Mr Toad!

*Toad leaps on to the canopy above the judge and twiddles the judge's wig
back to front.*

> The judge was apoplectic.
> They thought he might explode.

JUDGE. SIXTY YEARS!

TOAD.

> He'd never been faced
> With a prisoner as bold
> Or as brave as Mr Toad.

JUDGE. SEVENTY!

Toad grabs the chandelier and swings above the policemen.

TOAD.

> The police could never catch him!
> He was so nimble-toed!

JUDGE. EIGHTY!

*The court is now jammed shoulder-to-shoulder with policemen. Toad lets
go and springs nimbly over the sea of heads.*

TOAD.

> He escaped from their clutches
> For none knows as much as
> Amazing Mr Toad!

JUDGE. NINETY!

A boat-hook suddenly catches Toad's jacket, and he finds himself flying above the policemen's grasping hands.

TOAD.

> The officers couldn't believe it.
> They oohed! and ahhhed! and ohhed!
> As high up above them he flew like a bird
> > *(Toad realises he's caught.)*
> The . . . incredible . . . Mr . . . Toad . . .

The weasels haul Toad up. The spirit goes out of him.

WEASELS. A HUNDRED!

JUDGE. Done! ONE HUNDRED YEARS! Take him away!

Toad is dragged in chains through the gates of a medieval castle by two prison guards.

TOAD. Have mercy! Do not incarcerate me in a foul and darksome dungeon! Ah, I'll reform. Do not immure me hidden from the precious light of the sun!

There is a crash of thunder, a flash of lightning. Toad Hall appears somehow threatening in the darkness. Mole and Rat sit before a fire in the great hall. Thunder crashes and rain lashes the window panes. Rat is uncharacteristically gloomy.

RAT. It's all my fault, Mole. If I hadn't left Toad alone . . . All for a picnic . . .

MOLE. There must be something we can do, Ratty?

RAT. The minute we leave Toad Hall empty the weasels will be in here like . . . weasels.

MOLE. Ratty? I don't know but . . . Couldn't we spring Toad from jail?

RAT. How? He's in the strongest prison in the land.

MOLE. Well . . . I may not be very b-brave, Rat, but I *could* dig a tunnel.

RAT *(his whiskers crinkle up).* Moley! We're river-bank animals. We don't belong out there. *(He straightens them.)*

MOLE. What was that?

RAT. Just my whiskers, Mole.

MOLE. No. I heard something, Rat.

RAT. We'd best stay here and guard Toad Hall.

MOLE. Look out!

The doors burst open and the windows smash. There are weasels everywhere, sliding down curtains and bell-pulls. One comes down the chimney.

CHIEF WEASEL. You're trespassing. This is a weasel-only area.

ST JOHN WEASEL. And that means nobody's allowed here except weasels!

CHIEF WEASEL *(gives him a withering look)*. What else could it mean?

ST JOHN WEASEL. Just making sure they got the point.

Rat and Mole are thrown out. St John Weasel appears outside.

ST JOHN WEASEL. All unloaded, Chief!

A lorry stands outside the front door. It is stacked high with barrels labelled DANGER! EXPLOSIVES. *The Chief Weasel examines them.*

CHIEF WEASEL *(turning on St John Weasel)*. You idiot! *Those* are meant to be unloaded *here*, and the bones are to go over to the factory.

The Chief Weasel indicates a stack of barrels marked BONES, *then turns on his heel and disappears inside.*

ST JOHN WEASEL. Sorry, Chief! We'll change 'em over. *(Under his breath.)* After dinner.

The door slams. Scrawled across it is PRIVATE. WEASELS ONLY. *Rat and Mole pick themselves up, and examine the barrels.*

MOLE. What do you think they're up to, Rat?

RAT. Whatever it is, let's make it easier for them.

Rat experimentally peels a label off a 'Bones' barrel and sticks it on the 'Danger! Explosives' barrel. And vice versa.

MOLE. Why are you doing that, Ratty?

RAT. If in doubt, Mole, it often pays to keep weasels confused. Stay one ahead of their game – whatever it is.

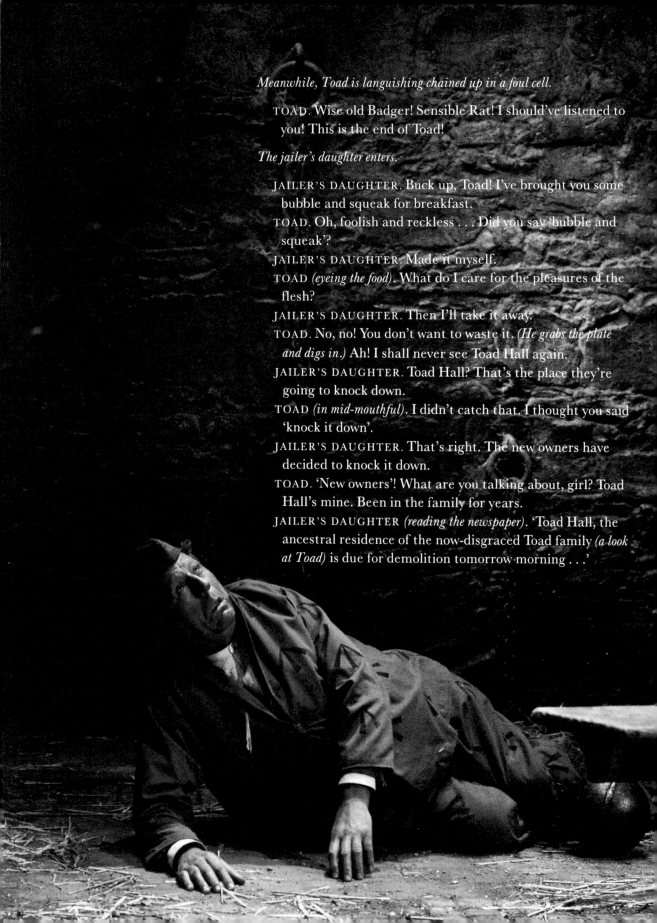

Meanwhile, Toad is languishing chained up in a foul cell.

TOAD. Wise old Badger! Sensible Rat! I should've listened to you! This is the end of Toad!

The jailer's daughter enters.

JAILER'S DAUGHTER. Buck up, Toad! I've brought you some bubble and squeak for breakfast.

TOAD. Oh, foolish and reckless . . . Did you say 'bubble and squeak'?

JAILER'S DAUGHTER. Made it myself.

TOAD *(eyeing the food)*. What do I care for the pleasures of the flesh?

JAILER'S DAUGHTER. Then I'll take it away.

TOAD. No, no! You don't want to waste it. *(He grabs the plate and digs in.)* Ah! I shall never see Toad Hall again.

JAILER'S DAUGHTER. Toad Hall? That's the place they're going to knock down.

TOAD *(in mid-mouthful)*. I didn't catch that. I thought you said 'knock it down'.

JAILER'S DAUGHTER. That's right. The new owners have decided to knock it down.

TOAD. 'New owners'! What are you talking about, girl? Toad Hall's mine. Been in the family for years.

JAILER'S DAUGHTER *(reading the newspaper)*. 'Toad Hall, the ancestral residence of the now-disgraced Toad family *(a look at Toad)* is due for demolition tomorrow morning . . .'

Apoplectic, Toad grabs the newspaper from her and reads on.

TOAD. 'Weasels, who took the property over when Mr Toad
    defaulted on repayment of six new motor cars, say it will be
    reduced to rubble within fifteen seconds . . .'

JAILER'S DAUGHTER *(cheerfully)*. They're going to blow it up.

TOAD. Blow up Toad Hall!

JAILER'S DAUGHTER. Wonderful what they can do now,
    innit?

*In his mind Toad sees a charming picture of Toad Hall hanging in a
Home Sweet Home-style frame hanging on the wall of his cell. Then he
sees it blow up.*

TOAD. My father's home. My sacred trust. Blown to
    smithereens! And it's all my fault.

JAILER'S DAUGHTER. Then you'd better stop 'em.

TOAD. Talk sense, girl. What can I do – incarcerated here?
    Oh, Unhappy Toad!

JAILER'S DAUGHTER *(sitting beside Toad)*. Look, Toad. I can't
    help feeling sorry for you. In fact, truth to tell, I'm really
    quite fond of you.

TOAD *(turning into Clark Gable)*. It's true. Ladies find me
    irresistible. *(He slips his arm around the jailer's daughter.)*

JAILER'S DAUGHTER. Now stop that!

TOAD. Tell me – which of my many features do you find *most*
    irresistible?

JAILER'S DAUGHTER. I can't think while you're gabbing.

TOAD. Ah! The power of love!

*The jailer's daughter leaps up from the bench which tips and deposits
Toad on the floor – bubble and squeak all over him.*

JAILER'S DAUGHTER. My aunt's a tea lady.

TOAD. Well, that's nothing to boast about.

JAILER'S DAUGHTER. She's very poor and you're very rich –
    or so you keep telling me.

TOAD. Yes, I am! I've simply pots of money . . .

JAILER'S DAUGHTER. Well, then . . .

*Outside the castle, Rat is peering down a freshly dug hole. Suddenly
Mole's head appears.*

MOLE. We're there, Ratty. I could hear Toad's voice right
    above me.

RAT. Well done, Mole. *(He starts to climb into the hole.)*

RAT. Well . . . come on.

MOLE *(he's scared stiff)*. Oh, Ratty . . .

RAT. This was *your* idea, Mole.

MOLE. It was . . . but . . .

RAT. We can't leave Toad in there twiddling his thumbs
while the weasels blow up Toad Hall.

*Meanwhile, the jailer's daughter has just introduced her aunt, the tea
lady, to Toad. Toad is aghast. A tea trolley stands nearby.*

TOAD. You don't expect *me* to dress up like *that?*

JAILER'S DAUGHTER. Then you can stay here twiddling your
thumbs while the weasels blow up Toad Hall. *(She starts to
hustle her aunt out.)*

TOAD. No, No! *(He reluctantly lays some coins on the table.)*
There's your five guineas. *(He looks on with contempt as the tea
lady snatches up the money.)*

JAILER'S DAUGHTER. Now take that off. *(She divests Toad of
his prison clothes and then his jacket.)*

TOAD. Careful! All my money's in there. *(Bitterly.)* What's
left of it.

JAILER'S DAUGHTER. Put your arm in here.

A flagstone at the back of the cell lifts and Mole peeps out fearfully. He takes in the scene and retreats immediately into the tunnel.

MOLE. Oh, Ratty. There are two women with him.

RAT. Two women? What are they doing?

MOLE *(in disbelief)*. They're . . . taking his clothes off!

RAT. What? *(He takes a quick incredulous look.)* Now they're dressing him up in women's clothes!

MOLE. Perhaps it's some sort of torture?

JAILER'S DAUGHTER. There! Alike as two pins. *(Toad and the tea lady are now dressed identically.)*

TEA LADY. I don't look like *that*!

TOAD. It's *me* that doesn't look like *that*!

JAILER'S DAUGHTER. Stop it, you two! Now. You tie Auntie up, while I make sure the coast is clear.

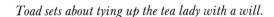

Toad sets about tying up the tea lady with a will.

TEA LADY. If I thought I looked *that* ugly I'd be only too glad to stay in jail . . .

JAILER'S DAUGHTER. And don't forget to gag her.

TOAD. Nothing would give me greater pleasure.

The jailer's daughter leaves.

TEA LADY. I mean talk about the back of a bus. I'm surprised people don't catch you to Trafalgar Square. No! Help!

TOAD *(getting carried away)*. Silence, old hag! Your screams are of no avail against the desperate Toad!

RAT. Psst! Toad!

TOAD. Who's that?

RAT. It's me! Over here!

TOAD. Ratty! What on earth are you doing?

RAT. Rescuing you. Come on!

TOAD. Don't need rescuing, Ratty! Got a clever plan all worked out myself!

RAT. But Toad. All you've got to do is follow me. Mole's dug this tunnel . . .

TOAD. Tunnel! Pooh! You'll not catch me sneaking out down a *tunnel*.

RAT. Toad! Stop being so fat-headed . . .

TOAD. A *tunnel*'s no way for an animal of my mettle to escape. We Toads do things with a bit more dash. A bit more zing!

RAT. Toad!

But it's too late. The jailer's daughter has returned. Rat hurriedly retreats.

JAILER'S DAUGHTER. The coast's clear.

The tea lady struggles and tries to call the jailer's daughter's attention to Rat and the tunnel.

JAILER'S DAUGHTER. Good luck, Toad.

For a moment it looks as if she might kiss him but Toad leaves. Back in the tunnel, Rat turns to Mole in dismay.

RAT. He won't come!

In the cell Toad's jacket, with his wallet, is still hanging on a chair. Toad walks confidently down a corridor, rounds a corner and sees a sentry ahead. Suddenly all his confidence evaporates. Every time he puts his hands on the trolley it rattles.

SENTRY. Why, if it isn't my sweetheart.
TOAD. Would you like some tea?
SENTRY. Where's my kiss?
TOAD *(genuinely shocked)*. Kiss? I'll give you a thump.
SENTRY. You *always* give me a kiss.

Toad pours tea and regards the greasy, unshaven sentry.

TOAD. I must be mad!

Toad hands over the cup of tea with a shakey hand. It rattles.

SENTRY. You don't seem to be quite yourself today, Granny.
TOAD. On the contrary – I'm more *myself* today.
SENTRY. How's that?
TOAD *(seductively)*. Because when I'm *really* myself, I give cheeky guards something special.
SENTRY. And what's that? *(He smiles and puckers his lips for a kiss.)*
TOAD. My warmest regards.

Toad pulls out the top of the sentry's trousers and turns on the tap of the tea urn, squirting hot tea into them.

SENTRY. Yiiiiih!
TOAD *(suddenly realising what he's done)*. Oh, cripes!

He breaks into a run, still pushing his trolley, and disappears round the corner. He runs out of the building and round another corner. A moment later the scalded sentry and several guards burst out of the door, and chase after him. Toad finds himself in a dead end. He looks for escape but can see none. He races up to the castle wall. It's too high. The guards appear round the corner and raise their halberds.

TOAD. Oh, cripes!
GUARD. Stop right there! You can't escape!
TOAD. Nincompoops!

Toad turns around to the wall and opens his mouth. His long prehensile

tongue curls up to the top of the wall and wraps itself around a spike. He swallows and hauls himself up. The guards stare in a mixture of disbelief and disgust.

GUARD. Erghhh! Gross!
SENTRY. Dis-gusting!

Toad drops down on the other side of the castle wall, just as Rat and Mole climb out of the tunnel.

TOAD. Hello, you fellows?

All the prison alarms go off. Shouts and clamour.

RAT. Come on!

They run for all they're worth.

RAT. What did you have to try and escape for?
TOAD. You don't think I'd sit in there twiddling my thumbs while the weasels blow up Toad Hall, do you?
RAT. No, of course not.

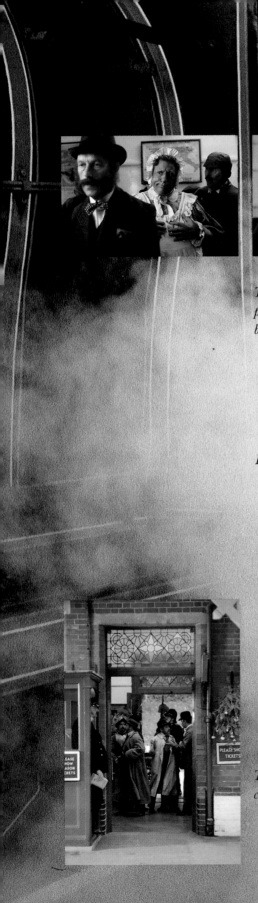

They arrive, breathless, in the booking hall of a railway station. Toad pushes aside an elderly gentleman and rushes up to the window. The booking clerk takes his time.

TOAD. Oh, do hurry up!

RAT *(whispering)*. Toad. Stop drawing attention to yourself.

TOAD. Well, one expects a certain standard of service, you know.

RAT. Not *now*!

Rat rolls his eyes.

TOAD. Can't you serve quicker than this, my man?

RAT. Toad. Just get the tickets.

BOOKING CLERK. Where to?

TOAD. Three to Toad-in-the-Wold. First class.

BOOKING CLERK. First class is five and nine each, Granny.

MOLE *(it's a fortune to him)*. Five and ninepence!

TOAD. That's nothing to me, I can assure you. *(Searching for his waistcoat.)* I've got it here. It's in my . . . oh . . . my wallet!

ELDERLY GENTLEMAN *(poking Toad with his umbrella)*. Do get a move on, madam.

TOAD. Look here, my man. Give me the tickets and I'll send the money on tomorrow.

BOOKING CLERK *(putting the tickets away)*. Next!

TOAD. This is an emergency!

ELDERLY GENTLEMAN. Move over, madam.

Toad is unceremoniously shoved away from the ticket window. A police car pulls up outside the station. Mole sees it.

MOLE. Look out!

TOAD. Arrrgh! The hounds of the law.

RAT. Ssh, Toad.

Rat bundles Toad on to the platform. The three race down the stairs and up on to the platform, where Rat pushes Toad and Mole into a doorway. Rat and Mole reappear very quickly. It's the Ladies. Toad (still dressed as a tea lady) comes out chatting to another woman who wags her finger at Rat and Mole. Toad does the same. Rat pulls Toad into another doorway. It's the Gents.

TOAD. Do you mind? I can't go in there.

Two policemen, the sentry and two detectives appear on the platform. They look around and then run down the stairs. Rat drags Toad and Mole behind some crates.

MOLE. Oh, Ratty. What are we going to do?

The train comes into the station just as their pursuers appear at the other end of the platform.

TOAD. I'll never see Toad Hall again except as a heap of rubble. Boooo-hoooooo! Arrgh!
RAT. Keep your voice down, Toad.

Toad blows his nose. Making exactly the same terrible noise, the engine vents steam, knocking Toad across the platform. The engine driver, a soft-hearted man, jumps out.

ENGINE DRIVER. I'm *so* sorry, madam. I didn't see you.

Toad opens one eye and looks slyly at the engine driver. Behind, the police are working their way down the platform.

TOAD. I'm a poor tea lady who's lost all her money, and unless I can get back tonight, I'll lose my home as well.
ENGINE DRIVER. That's terrible.
TOAD. Our wicked landlord will blow it up.
ENGINE DRIVER. No!

Toad bursts into an exaggerated howl of misery.

ENGINE DRIVER. Look here, missus. Keep quiet and I'll let you and your children ride in my cab.
RAT. 'Children'?

Toad is on his feet, his eyes shining like a schoolboy's.

TOAD. Ride in your cab?
ENGINE DRIVER. It's against company regulations, but . . . 'Ere, hang on!

Toad is already on board, pulling at the train's whistle.

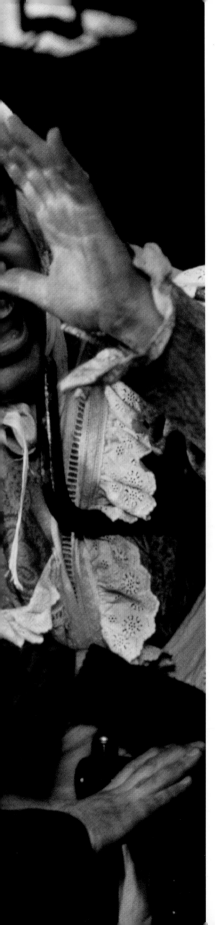

TOAD. All aboard!

RAT. Keep your head in, you idiot.

TOAD *(to the elderly gentleman)*. No room for you, codface.

RAT. Toad!

ENGINE DRIVER. Toad?

SENTRY *(spotting Toad)*. There he is!

TOAD. Yipes! How does this thing work? *(He desperately throws every knob he can get his hands on.)*

ENGINE DRIVER. Don't touch *anything*!

But the train starts moving. The passengers scramble. Whistles blow. The sentry, a guard, two detectives and a policeman jump into the last carriage.

As the train thunders down the track, the pursuers are making their way towards the engine. Toad peers out through the window, his eyes round as saucers.

TOAD. Faster! Make it go *faster*!

RAT. Toad! You're meant to be my mother.

TOAD. Oh, phooey!

Toad helps the engine driver shovel coal. Mole hears a shout. The sentry is waving out of a window in the first carriage.

SENTRY. Halt this train!

MOLE. Why's that passenger waving at us?

RAT *(pulling Mole to the floor)*. They're on the train!

ENGINE DRIVER. *Who's* on the train? *(He and Toad take a look.)*

A detective and a policeman have joined the sentry.

DETECTIVE. Stop this train!

ENGINE DRIVER. I'd better see what they want.

Toad flings himself at the engine driver, clasping his legs.

TOAD. Oh, no! Don't stop the train. Good, tender-hearted Mr Engine Driver.

ENGINE DRIVER. You'd better tell me what's going on.

The heroes look at each other. There's nothing else for it.

TOAD. Alas! I am not the simple tea lady I seem to be.

RAT. And we are certainly not his children.

TOAD. I am a toad, the well-known and popular Mr Toad, a landed proprietor. At least, I was until weasels stole my ancestral home.

MOLE. They're going to blow it up tomorrow morning unless we can stop them.

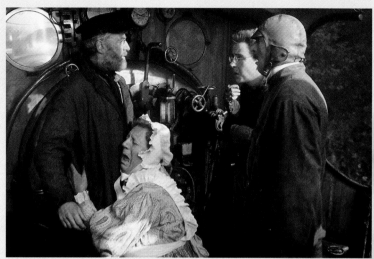

ENGINE DRIVER *(nodding to their pursuers)*. Who are *they*?

TOAD. My evil-hearted tormentors who wish to drag me back to their loathsome dungeon.

ENGINE DRIVER. A jail-bird eh?

TOAD. All I did was borrow a motor car . . .

ENGINE DRIVER. I don't hold with motor cars.

TOAD. Oh! Neither do I.

A gunshot rings out.

ENGINE DRIVER. What's that? *(He looks out, but ducks back as another bullet pings off the polished metal engine.)*

TOAD *(craftily)*. They've no respect for public transport, that lot. All they care about is cars!

ENGINE DRIVER. Nobody shoots at *my* engine. *(He sticks his head out, incensed.)* Hey! Stop that!

FIRST DETECTIVE. You stop this train!

He fires again. Mole cowers.

ENGINE DRIVER. That paintwork's brand new!

He scrambles on to the tender and starts lobbing lumps of coal. With unerring accuracy he knocks the pistol out of the first detective's hand with the first throw. With the next, he 'skims' a lump of coal so it hits one – two – three heads sticking out of the windows. They promptly go back in, but the now incandescent engine driver hangs off the side of the tender, and lobs coal through the window of the carriage hitting the sentry.

SENTRY. Ow! *(He slams the window up.)*

ENGINE DRIVER. Motorists! Headlight flashers! Road-lovers! I'll show you! I'll . . .

But then disaster strikes. The train passes a mail-net which neatly scoops the engine driver off the side of the tender.

RAT. We've lost the driver.

TOAD. Yipppeeee! *(He eagerly throws himself at the controls.)* I found it! I found it!

MOLE. What – the brake?

TOAD. The accelerator!

MOLE. No, Toad.

Toad starts to push the train faster and faster. The second detective has climbed out of the carriage door. Rat spots this. He climbs on to the tender and starts lobbing coal at the second detective. Toad is now driving at such a reckless speed that Rat is almost shaken off.

RAT. Toad! We'll come off the rails!

TOAD. Seventy miles an hour!

RAT *(pressing a lump of coal into Mole's paw)*. Moley. Keep me covered.

MOLE. I can't throw for toffee.

RAT. Just throw.

Mole throws but the coal only lands a few feet away. Rat climbs down between the tender and carriage, as the train sways dangerously.

RAT. Slow down, Toad! *(Toad is in a world of his own.)*

TOAD. Eighty miles an hour!

Rat tries to uncouple the carriage from the tender.

TOAD. Eighty-five! I wonder if it can do a hundred?

MOLE. Look out, Ratty!

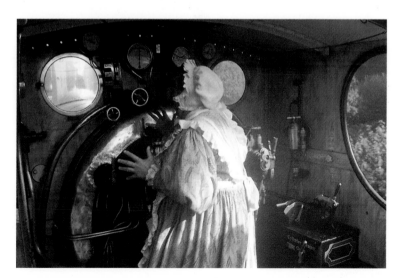

The second detective suddenly appears round the corner of the carriage pointing his gun at Rat.

SECOND DETECTIVE. Stop that! I'll shoot!

The noise is deafening, the speed terrifying.

TOAD. Ninety! *(He notices a lever.)* I wonder what that does? *(He pulls it.)*

There is a terrible screeching.

SECOND DETECTIVE. I have given you an official warning. I shall now proceed to shoot.

He prepares to fire. The train shudders and jerks and the second detective is thrown off, dropping his pistol on the running board.

TOAD. Errrrgh! It's the *brake*! Don't want that.

Toad releases the brake. The train leaps forward. Rat has the coupling pin halfway out. He realises he must get the gun.

RAT. Moley! Come and give me a hand.
MOLE. Oh, no!
RAT. Mole! You've got to.
MOLE. Ratty, I can't . . .
RAT. Yes, you *can*, Mole!

The terrified Mole clambers towards Rat. The second detective's gun is almost joggled off. The sentry is now trying to reach it.

RAT. That's it, Moley.

Finally Mole makes it and Rat hands him the coupling pin. The sentry has almost got his hand on the pistol. Rat dives for it but the train rattles and the pistol is joggled off on to a ledge. Both Rat and the sentry lunge for it, but it falls off. So does the sentry.

MOLE. Rat!

The same bump has jogged the coupling pin out of its socket and Mole is now desperately trying to get it back in – but a gap is opening up between the tender and the carriage. Mole is straddling the gap.

TOAD. Ninety-one! Ninety-two! Why won't it go faster?
RAT. Slow down, Toad!

Mole's feet are getting further apart. He is going to have to jump one way or the other. He drops the pin. His arms windmill as he loses balance. In the nick of time Rat pulls him on to the carriage. Toad suddenly finds he can push the accelerator up.

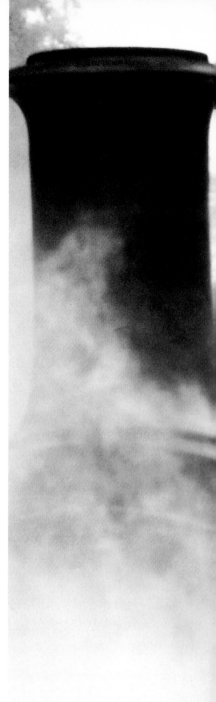

TOAD. Ninety-five! Ninety-six! Hey! It *is* going faster. Hooray!

The engine, unencumbered by its carriages, picks up speed. Rat and Mole are marooned on the carriage.

TOAD *(in seventh heaven)*. A hundred! This is *fantastic*, Ratty. A hundred and one! A hundred and two!

Rat and Mole are on the carriage buffers.

MOLE. I'm so sorry, Ratty.
RAT. You did jolly well, Mole.
MOLE. I ruined your plan.
FIRST DETECTIVE *(pointing a gun at them)*. Hands up!

The first detective, the guard and the policeman are all on the carriage roof. Toad is still oblivious to all.

TOAD. Oooooh! A hundred and five!

Suddenly the engine disappears into a tunnel. It comes out the other end and races down the line, far too fast. Toad is delighted.

TOAD. A hundred and seven! A hundred and ten! Yeeeeaaahhh! A hundred and twenty! Ratty! *(He turns.)* Ratty?

The engine swings crazily round a bend, out of control. It disappears. There is a sickening crash. Then the engine is discovered upside down at the bottom of the embankment, its wheels spinning. Meanwhile, Rat and Mole are cowering on the carriage with their hands up.

FIRST DETECTIVE. You're both under arrest.

Suddenly they disappear into the tunnel with a crunch. When the train comes out the other end, Rat and Mole are still on the carriage but there is no one on the carriage roof. Their pursuers are spread-eagled on a ledge above the tunnel. Further down the track, the ecstatic face of Toad emerges from underneath the capsized engine. He looks round and begins to realise that not only is he alive and well – he is also free.

TOAD *(singing)*.
> Oh, nobody knew how to catch him,
> So clever and nimble-toed!
> They couldn't snitch or snatch him,
> That elusive Mr Toad!
> > *(He dances off down the road.)*

The carriages have now come to a halt. Mole and Rat hop off.

RAT. We'd better find Badger . . . Mole?

Rat turns to find Mole digging frantically in the ground.

RAT. Mole! *(He tries to stop Mole digging.)*

MOLE. I'm not brave like you, Ratty. I'm not strong and fierce like Badger.

RAT. You were very brave, Moley.

MOLE *(tears in his eyes)*. I'm just a 'spineless nobody'. You don't want someone like me as a friend. *(He desperately starts digging again.)*

RAT. Don't talk nonsense, Moley. What are you doing?

MOLE. I'm going home, Ratty. I'm sorry.

RAT. Moley!

Mole disappears into the ground. Rat can't stop him.

Elsewhere Toad, still dressed as a tea lady, is footsore and getting crosser by the minute. The sun is a great know-all.

SUN. Going 'home' are we, Toad?

TOAD *(testily)*. Yes.

SUN. Better hurry. I'll be setting soon.

TOAD. How far is Toad Hall?

SUN *(looking to see)*. A long way yet.

TOAD. Ohhh . . .

SUN. Yes, I can see everything from up here. That's the great thing about being the sun.

TOAD. Can you see what the weasels are up to?

SUN *(taking a look)*. Putting the dynamite into Toad Hall.

TOAD. Dynamite!

SUN *(mischievously)*. Oooh! I'm beginning to set.

TOAD *(sinking in despair on a milestone)*. All is lost. Wretched Toad!

SUN. Shouldn't have gone round stealing motor cars.

TOAD *(glowering)*. Didn't.

SUN. Did.

TOAD. Didn't.

SUN. I saw it all . . . Did.

Toad glowers. The sun smiles – he won that argument.

TOAD. Oh, go away!

SUN. Not until it's time.

The sound of a lorry attracts Toad. He jumps up to hail it.

TOAD. Ha ha! Toad's luck again! I'll spin 'em one of my highly successful yarns . . . *(He lies in the road. The lorry pulls up short. It is full of weasels.)* Oh help! I'm a poor old tea lady who can't get home . . . Yipes! It's you!

CHIEF WEASEL. Toad. What are you doing out of jail?

TOAD. Ha! I escaped by great daring and cunning! And I demand you hand back Toad Hall immediately.

CHIEF WEASEL. Of course. It's all yours.

TOAD *(wrong-footed)*. Oh . . .

ST JOHN WEASEL. We were just looking after it for you, Toady, while you were in jail.

TOAD. Oh . . . Thanks.

CHIEF WEASEL. Why are you dressed like that, Toad?

TOAD. Master of disguise! Fooled everyone!

ST JOHN WEASEL. You're a clever one and no mistake, Toad.

TOAD. Yes. Drove a train. Just like that.

CHIEF WEASEL. Did you. Well, we've got a new motor we'd like you to test for us.

He nods towards a huge and ominous-looking machine, covered by a sheet, on the back of the lorry.

TOAD. A new motor? Rather!

ST JOHN WEASEL. Well . . . It's *got* a motor.

TOAD. Sort of experimental, it it?

CHIEF WEASEL. That's it.

TOAD. Oh, good!

The weasels hustle Toad into the lorry and drive off. On the back is a sign which reads: GIANT MINCING MACHINES LTD.

Rat is running as hard as he can through the Wild Wood. Suddenly, to his surprise, the Wild Wood comes to an end. He stares around in disbelief. A swathe of destruction has been cut right through the middle of the Wild Wood. Something catches Rat's eye. He stoops and picks up a broken sign. It reads: MR BADGER. STRICTLY NO VISITORS. *Suddenly a voice behind him makes him jump.*

RAT. Badger!

Badger is standing outside his front door. The bell-pull hangs at a crazy angle. The door is half-off its hinges. Rat is speechless. He looks around at the desolation.

BADGER. Yesterday they destroyed Mole End. Tomorrow Toad Hall. Today it's the Wild Wood . . . No. I can't have that . . .

Meanwhile, inside their dog-food factory, the weasels are making last-minute adjustments. Suddenly the lift doors open and Toad is bundled in by Clarence, Geoffrey and St John Weasel.

> TOAD. Funny-looking motor. How's it work?
>
> CHIEF WEASEL. Let me show you, Toad. The motor drives this wheel here. That turns the axle – attached to which are these blades in there.
>
> TOAD. Yes, I see them.
>
> CHIEF WEASEL. They rotate. And this screw squeezes the raw material through those holes.
>
> TOAD. Sort of mincing machine, is it?
>
> CHIEF WEASEL. Smart fellow.
>
> TOAD. Yes, I always was rather quick on the uptake. But where do I fit in?

Toad looks innocently at St John and the other weasels. They snigger. The Chief Weasel sweeps out, followed by Clarence and Geoffrey.

Rat and Badger's boat arrives at the steps below Toad Hall. The two heroes hide as two drunken weasel guards, singing tunelessly, stagger towards them. Rat is shocked.

RAT. They're all drunk!

BADGER. Good. They aren't expecting any visitors.

The guards turn before they reach the steps. Badger disappears from sight. Rat hears two clunks.

RAT. I say! Badger . . .

The weasels' legs are dragged into the bushes. A few moments later, Rat and Badger appear from the undergrowth near the front of the house. They are now dressed as weasel guards. Rat trips on something. He bends down and picks up some cable. He pulls it – it runs off towards Toad's meadow.

RAT. Would you excuse me, Badger? *(He bites through the cable and heads towards the meadow.)*

BADGER. What on earth are you up to, Rat?

RAT. I'm not sure, but I *hope* I'm keeping the weasels confused. *(He disappears, coiling the wire as he goes.)*

BADGER. Ratty!

Meanwhile, Mole breaks through the wall of his destroyed home. He looks around at the pathetic remains of his house.

MOLE. I tried to be like you, Ratty, but I'm not. I belong here. Underground. Oh . . . I'm sorry, Ratty, my dear friend . . .

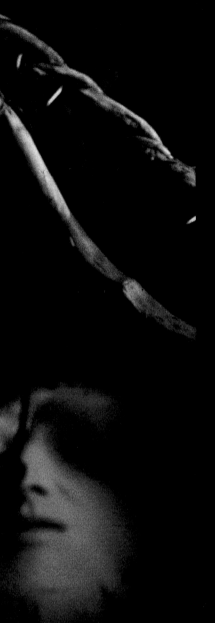

Tears run down his face as he kneels to wipe the dust from the face of his clock. It mutters, 'Tea-time,' and expires. Suddenly a light flashing through the door catches Mole's attention. He goes out through his ruined garden and down his broken tunnel towards the light.

At Toad Hall, lights are blazing everywhere. In the windows we see the silhouettes of carousing weasels. There is drunken singing and quarrelling. A window is smashed, followed by raucous laughter. National Front-style weasel guards are posted all round the perimeter of the grounds. There is barbed wire and a watch-tower with a searchlight. Badger and Rat appear from round a corner. They march to the bridge where a drunken weasel sentry stands in a sentry box. He raises a glass of wine to them.

DRUNKEN GUARD. Have a drink! Hic!

BADGER. No, thank you. (Rat and Badger try to pass.)

DRUNKEN GUARD. Wait! You're funny-looking weasels. (Suddenly he notices Rat's tail running over his shoe.) Hey! You aren't weasels at all.

BADGER (pointing behind the guard). Well, who are they, then?

The drunken guard turns. Badger and Rat tip him head first into the moat. The wine goes over Badger's coat.

RAT. You can get that off with a little salt.

BADGER. Now let's find the Chief Weasel.

CHIEF WEASEL. He's right behind you.

They spin round to find themselves confronted by the Chief Weasel and Clarence and Geoffrey Weasel.

Mole's face appears from the molehill. All is dark and quiet, but Mole can make out the weasels' factory and the earth-movers that he thought were monsters. He rubs his glasses and peers at a noticeboard. A search-light sweeps across and momentarily illuminates it.

MOLE (reading). Dog-food factory? Dog-food factory! (An overwhelming anger sweeps through his body.) They knocked in my home to build a dog-food factory!

Suddenly he hears shouts: the Chief Weasel and company are pushing Badger and Rat towards the factory. Mole runs up to the doors but they are locked. He looks up at the scaffolding surrounding the factory. His only chance is to climb up to that lighted window. The first bar of scaffolding is too high, but there is a water butt nearby. Mole climbs on to that and so on up the scaffolding.

MOLE. Dog-food factory!

Finally, he reaches the window and peers in. Toad, his hands tied, is hooked on to a runner for carcasses.

TOAD. Desist! No ! Help!

ST JOHN WEASEL. We want you to see how the mincer works, Toad – from the inside! Pond-lover! Fly-eater!

St John Weasel throws a switch. There is a terrible noise as the mincer starts. As Mole desperately wonders what he can do to save Toad, the Chief Weasel (accompanied by two other weasels) pushes Rat and Badger into the mincing room.

CHIEF WEASEL. Wait! *(He hits the* OFF *switch.)* I've got a better recipe. Put 'em all in together!

Rat's whiskers crinkle up. The weasels snigger.

ST JOHN WEASEL. Oooh, la la! *Très haute cuisine!*

CHIEF WEASEL. Shut up! *(He goes right up to Badger and Rat.)* You know, you've convinced me. I'm not going to blow up Toad Hall tomorrow, after all. I'm going to blow it up tonight! *(He yanks Rat's whiskers straight.)* Make 'em into sausages and slice 'em up!

He sweeps out. Badger and Rat are hooked on the rail in front of Toad, who has been up to the mincer and back. A weasel starts the mincer again. The hooks carry our heroes towards it.

MOLE. Where's that Mole spirit?

He hesitates no longer. He drops through the window. The weasels stand on a ramp by the mincer, jeering. They don't notice Mole. He can see the OFF *switch. Badger is almost at the mincer. But as he dashes for the switch, his scarf catches in the gearing and he can't quite reach it. The scarf is tightening round his neck.*

Inside the great hall at Toad Hall the weasels are all drunk and sitting on the barrels of gunpowder smoking cigars. It's a dangerous place. One weasel is playing the piano with an axe. Others are throwing bottles. Plates of food and glasses hit the portraits and armorial bearings. The Chief Weasel enters and takes his position at the head table.

CLARENCE WEASEL. Quiet! The Chief has an announcement.

GEOFFREY WEASEL. Yes. Quiet! The Chief has an announcement.

CLARENCE WEASEL. Shut up!

CHIEF WEASEL. Gentlemen. Fellow members of Weasel Developments Ltd. The dog-food factory is in production as from a few moments ago! *(Drunken cheering.)* The demolition of this building, to make way for our abattoir, capable of processing all forms of river-dwelling animal, has been brought forward to tonight. *(Wild hooting and cheering.)* In exactly fifteen minutes, Toad Hall will be history!

The weasels go wild with excitement. Food flies through the air.

CHIEF WEASEL. Settle down.

Badger is dropped! But just as he falls, he gets his hands free, catches the sides and spread-eagles his body across the mouth of the mincer. The screw rotates savagely beneath him. The weasels boo and cat-call and start to throw things. Rat lands on top of Badger. Mole is being strangled and dragged into the gears. Badger can barely carry the weight of himself and now Rat. At this moment Toad falls on top of them. Badger can't hold on! Mole has found the whitewash brush in his pocket. He lifts it to stick it in the gearing, but his sleeve gets caught in another part.

St John throws a spanner at Toad, concussing him. The spanner falls into the mincer with a terrible grinding. The machinery jumps, releasing Mole's sleeve. In a flash Mole inserts the brush into the gearing where his scarf is caught and that too jumps. He pulls the scarf free. Badger can hold on no longer. But just as they all fall towards the mincer screw Mole hits the OFF switch and the machinery stops. The weasels jeer. Then, realising someone has interfered, they spin round to find Mole with a shotgun.

> ST JOHN WEASEL. Better put that down before someone
>   gets hurt, Moley.
> MOLE. I'll sh-sh-shoot.
> ST JOHN WEASEL. But you've only got one shot.

As Mole hesitates, Badger, Rat and Toad emerge from the mincer.

> ST JOHN WEASEL. Give us the gun and we'll all be friends.
> MOLE. Friends! You said there was no such thing!
> ST JOHN WEASEL. Oh, come on! That was just an intro to a
>   song.
> MOLE. You destroyed my home to build a dog-meat factory!
> ST JOHN WEASEL. The area needs one. Our market research
>   shows . . .
> MOLE. You put my friends in your mincer!
> ST JOHN WEASEL. Just a harmless joke . . .

Suddenly Badger appears behind the three nameless weasels.

> BADGER. Well . . . Ha! – Ha! – Ha! (*At each 'Ha!' he throws a
>   weasel off the walkway.*)
> MOLE (*rather shocked*). I say . . . Badger!

Badger, with Rat and Toad, pushes St John Weasel towards Mole.

> ST JOHN WEASEL. I'm not really a weasel. I'm a rabbit. They
>   forced me to work in here. You saved me. Thank you!
>   Thank you!
> BADGER. Shut up! And keep moving.

Just as they get to the door, Toad notices a switch labelled AUTO.

TOAD. 'Auto'? Oh, good! We can drive back.
BADGER. No, Toad! Don't touch *anything*.

But it's too late. The ramp drops at one end and shoots them all into a lower mincer as it all starts up again. They leap for the sides.
    Back at Toad Hall, there is still chaos and confusion. Half the weasels are taking no notice of the Chief Weasel.

CHIEF WEASEL. I'm blowing this place up in ten minutes whether or not you lot are out of it. (*He makes to leave.*)
CLARENCE WEASEL. Wait, Chief! The boys have got a little surprise for you.
CHIEF WEASEL (*suspicious*). Surprise? It can wait ten minutes.
GEOFFREY WEASEL. No, no! We think you'd like it now.

Back at the factory, our heroes and St John Weasel are still hanging from the side of the mincer.

BADGER. You imbecile, Toad!
TOAD. Sorry! Sorry!
BADGER. I am never, *ever* going to try and help you again!
ST JOHN WEASEL. I'm slipping! Help! (*Rat helps him.*)

Suddenly there is a graunching noise and the higher mincer spits up the spanner. It falls into Mole's hand. He peers over the top.

RAT. How do we turn it off?
MOLE (*peering at the distant* OFF *switch which swims in his blurry vision*). Oh dear, oh dear. Can't throw for toffee.

Desperately he flings the spanner. In slow motion it curves through the air and – to Mole's utter surprise – hits the OFF *switch. The mincer stops.*

RAT (*appears above the side of the mincer*). Moley! Did *you* do that?
MOLE. Yes, Rat.

At Toad Hall, a cake in the shape of the Hall is wheeled in.

WEASELS. Happy birthday, Chief!

The weasels sing 'For He's a Jolly Good Weasel'. Some look puzzled.

GEOFFREY WEASEL. Three cheers for the Chief. Hip, hip!
WEASELS. Hooray!
CHIEF WEASEL (*strangely touched*). How did you know it was
   my birthday?
CLARENCE WEASEL. Aren't you going to blow 'em out?

*The Chief Weasel looks warily round, then shrugs, leans over the cake
and blows out the candles. Clarence Weasel dives for cover as the cake
explodes. The windows shatter. Clarence Weasel leaps on to the table.*

CLARENCE WEASEL. Too bad you couldn't stick around. I'm
   in charge now. Ha, ha, ha!
GEOFFREY WEASEL. No no no no! *I'm* in charge now.
CLARENCE WEASEL. What?
GEOFFREY WEASEL. Grab 'em, boys!

A fight breaks out among the weasels.

CLARENCE WEASEL. You devious . . . (*He lunges at Geoffrey.*)

Suddenly Toad, Badger, Rat and Mole charge in, firing into the ceiling.

BADGER. It's a shame *none* of you can stick around!

The weasels freeze. Clarence Weasel turns on Geoffrey Weasel.

CLARENCE WEASEL. Did you let them in here?
GEOFFREY WEASEL. 'Course I didn't!
CLARENCE WEASEL. Oh yes, you did. (*He hits him.*)
GEOFFREY WEASEL. Oh no, I didn't.

*Geoffrey Weasel and Clarence Weasel start to fight again. Badger bangs
two weasels' heads together. They turn and hit the weasels behind them.
Toad bangs a weasel over the head with a shield. The weasel spins and
hits another. Rat's sabre slashes a weasel's braces so his trousers fall.*

Another laughs and is hit by the first. Mole up-ends the table: Geoffrey and Clarence land in a thrashing heap. The weasels are now all fighting each other.

Badger and friends realise they don't need to do anything – so they form a chorus line and dance through the feuding weasels.

TOAD (*singing*).

    It's a pleasure to have you here, Mr Badger.

           (He clubs a weasel.)

BADGER (*singing*).

    So good of you to ask me, Mr Toad.

           (He bangs two weasels' heads together.)

RAT (*singing*).

    And as for dear old Mole

    I'm so glad you left your hole.

           (Mole despatches two weasels.)

MOLE (*singing, to Toad*).

    And came to join you here in your abode!

ALL FOUR.

    We were born on the same river bank.

    What's mine is yours is his!

           (They each bash a weasel.)

    Raised where the willows dip into the water,

    We get along like cheese and porter.

    Every morn we each give a thank

    For *friends* is what we is!

           (They each bash a weasel.)

Badger and company continue knocking out the weasels as if it were part of the dance routine. Meanwhile, however, the battered Chief Weasel has revived and is dragging himself towards the exit.

CHIEF WEASEL. You've got it coming to you, you garbage!

He staggers out of the great hall. Toad spots him and breaks away from the song and dance.

The Chief Weasel heads for the dog-food factory. Moments later Toad appears at the door. The Chief Weasel reaches the factory, runs round the scaffolding and in the door. Toad follows to find the door is locked. The Chief's head looks out from the scaffolding above. He holds the plunger for the explosives in his hands.

> CHIEF WEASEL. Now, Toad, you do the countdown.
> TOAD. Why . . . you . . . you . . . WEASEL!

Toad flings himself at the scaffolding and starts to climb.

> CHIEF WEASEL. Come on, Toad! You can count down from
> ten, surely. Ten . . . nine . . . Toad, where are you?

Toad is climbing as hard as he can.

> CHIEF WEASEL. If you won't do it, I'll have to do it myself.
> Eight . . . seven . . . six . . . Can you hear, Toad? . . . Five . . .
> Only four to go and goodbye Toad Hall! Four . . . Now what
> comes after four? Oh, I know . . . Three, two, ONE!

Suddenly, Toad's hand appears over the scaffolding and yanks the plunger away from the Chief Weasel.

> CHIEF WEASEL. Hey!

The Chief Weasel lunges at Toad who loses his footing and is left dangling. The plunger hangs from its line beside him. The Chief Weasel puts his face right up against Toad's.

> CHIEF WEASEL. Blowing up this dump is only the beginning.
> You won't recognise this place by the time I've finished!
> TOAD. But why? Why destroy this lovely place?
> CHIEF WEASEL. Because it'll make me extremely rich! (*He
> bites Toad's left hand.*)
> TOAD. Yeow!

Toad lets go with his left hand and in that instant the Chief Weasel bites his other hand. Toad lets go with that and plummets.

> CHIEF WEASEL. Sorry you couldn't stick around for the
> fireworks!

Toad lands in the water butt, smashing it. He looks up to see the Chief Weasel hauling up the plunger. The drenched Toad leaps to his feet and races off towards Toad Hall.

> TOAD. Badger! Ratty! Mole! Get out of there!

Badger, Rat and Mole are just concluding the song.

Back at the factory, the Chief Weasel has regained the detonator. He presses the plunger. Toad runs towards Toad Hall.

TOAD. Badger! GET OUT!

Suddenly there is an almighty explosion. For an instant Toad is lit up by the flash. A series of enormous explosions rocks the ground and a fireball looms in the distance above the trees, from the direction of Toad Hall. Toad is engulfed in dust and smoke and flying debris. He chokes and falls to the ground.

TOAD. Oh, my friends. It's all my fault! Badger. Ratty. Dear Mole. It's all my fault! (*He is convulsed by sobs.*)

Gradually, however, the smoke and dust clears and Toad looks up. Toad Hall is still standing. The front door bursts open. Badger, Rat and Mole appear.

BADGER. What the devil was that?

They all look in the direction of the dog-food factory – flames and smoke fill the air beyond the trees. The watch tower slowly collapses in the smoke. The sign reading 'Dog-Food Factory' slowly topples to the ground as well. Rat looks at Mole.

RAT. Well, it looks as if we confused those weasels good and proper.
MOLE. You mean . . . They put the explosives in the dog-meat factory, and . . . Oh, you clever old Ratty!
BADGER. You did well, Rat.

Next day, a rapturous Toad appears, to the sound of tumultuous applause.

TOAD. And so Toad Hall was saved by my daring and cleverness. I shall now narrate how I escaped from jail, stole a train and single-handedly defeated the weasels' plans to destroy the river bank.

There is more applause. Toad is using a phonograph for his audience as he practises his speech on a row of empty chairs.

TOAD. But first a little song . . .
BADGER. Oh, no, you won't!

Toad spins round to see Badger, Mole and Rat.

TOAD. Oh hello, you chaps?
BADGER. Toad. What are these? (*He waves an invitation card.*)

TOAD. My invitation cards? Something wrong with 'em?
BADGER. They are disgraceful. *(He reads.)*

Programme of Entertainment:
Speech . . . . by Toad
Song . . . . by Snr Enrico Toado
Conjuring Tricks . . . . . The Great Toadini
Juggling . . . . The Amazing Toadisto

Throughout this Toad has hung his head.

RAT. Now look here, Toad. Understand, there are going to be
no speeches and no songs.
TOAD. Mayn't I sing them just one *little* song?
RAT. Toady, you know your songs are self-praise, and . . .
BADGER. Gas.
RAT. You've *got* to turn over a new leaf.
MOLE. For all our sakes, Toady. *(Toad looks round at his friends.)*

*Some time later, there is a gay regatta of punts on the river in front of
Toad Hall. Everyone is there. Most of the rabbits are snogging. We hear
Toad's voice.*

TOAD. My friends. I am indeed a proud and stupid Toad. My
conceit and foolishness nearly cost me – nearly cost us all –
Toad Hall. Henceforth, I will be very different. No more
boasting, no more fads. I know now there is more to life
than motor cars.

The cheering is led by Mole and Badger and Rat.

RABBIT BAND *(dutifully).* Sing us a song, Mr Toad!
TOAD. No no no . . . no songs.

All the snogging rabbits look relieved.

BABY RABBIT. Oh, go on, Mr Toad!
RABBIT PARENTS. Ssh!
TOAD. Well . . . Maybe just a little one . . .

Everyone groans.

BADGER. Toad! You back-sliding . . .
TOAD. Come on, Badger.

Toad pulls the reluctant Badger on to the stage.

BADGER. Toad! How could you!
TOAD. You too, dear Ratty and dear Moley.

Reluctantly at first but then with growing enthusiasm, Badger and friends do a reprise of the River-bankers' Song.

BADGER, RAT, MOLE AND TOAD.
>We were born on the same river bank,
>What's mine is yours is his.
>Raised where the willows dip into the water,
>We get along like cheese and porter.
>Every morn we each give a thank
>That friends is what we is.

Toad's attention however, has been caught by a sound. He uncouples himself from his dancing friends and slips away to the courtyard. His eyes go round with excitement. There stands a gleaming new aeroplane.

TOAD. Rapture! Oh, poop-poop! Poop-poop!

The engine driver stands by as Toad leaps in. At the regatta everyone is just finishing the song as the plane soars over the top of Toad Hall. Everyone looks up astonished. The plane does a victory roll.

MOLE. It's Toad! Hooray!

Badger frowns. Rat's whiskers crinkle. Rabbits start in terror. Many fall into the river.

BADGER. That's the last time I ever try to help that . . . that . . . that . . . Ohhh!

The plane soars away into the skies. We follow it up and back down the river – across the same landscape as at the start – until we reach the coast and the plane flies off and out to sea.

THE WIND IN THE WILLOWS
Screenplay by Terry Jones
from the book by Kenneth Grahame
Produced by John Goldstone
and Jake Eberts
Directed by Terry Jones

Starring
Steve Coogan *Mole*, Eric Idle *Rat*, Terry Jones *Toad*,
Antony Sher *Chief Weasel*, Nicol Williamson *Badger*.

Guest stars
John Cleese *Defence Counsel*, Stephen Fry *Judge*,
Bernard Hill *Engine Driver*, Michael Palin *The Sun*,
Nigel Planer *Car Salesman*, Julia Sawalha *Jailer's
Daughter*, Victoria Wood *Tea Lady*.

with Robert Bathurst *St John Weasel*,
Don Henderson *Sentry*, Richard James *Geoffrey Weasel*
& *The Clock*, Keith-Lee Castle *Clarence Weasel*.

and Roger Ashton-Griffiths, Hugo Blick,
John Boswall, Sarah Crowden, David Hatton,
William Lawrance, John Levitt,
Graham McTavish, Bernard Padden,
Richard Ridings, Peter Whitfield.

Casting Irene Lamb
Make-up and hair design Jan Sewell
Director of photography David Tattersall BSC
Editor Julian Doyle
Production and costume design James Acheson
Original songs and music by Terry Jones,
John Du Prez, Andre Jacquemin, Dave Howman

First published in Great Britain in 1996
by Mandarin Paperbacks
an imprint of Reed International Books Ltd
Michelin House, 81 Fulham Road, London SW3 6RB
and Auckland, Melbourne, Singapore and Toronto

Copyright © 1996 Allied Filmmakers NV
All rights reserved

ISBN 0 7493 3670 6
A CIP catalogue record for this book
is available at the British Library

Designed by James Campus
Stills by Keith Hamshere

Typeset by Dorchester Typesetting Group Ltd
Printed and bound in Great Britain
by Jarrold and Sons Ltd